Poems & Rhymes & Things To Do Now That I'm A Toddler, Too

by Connie Smrke

Incentive Publications, Inc.
Nashville, Tennessee

Cover and illustrations by Gayle Seaberg Harvey
Edited by Jan Keeling

Library of Congress Catalog Card Number: 92-71472
ISBN 0-86530-107-7

Table of Contents

INTRODUCTION

Children enjoy learning in play situations and they respond to playful language. Vocabulary can be enriched and reinforced with easily-remembered rhymes and repetition. Using descriptive rhymes for creative movement and "acting-out" activities makes for personal involvement and connection. As children are allowed freedom to crawl, hop, walk, run, and skip while reciting verses or singing happy songs, positive attitudes toward learning will develop. Verses, action rhymes, and songs provide young children with enjoyable opportunities to practice body-part awareness, alphabet association, and number identification. Sharing, putting toys away, and using good manners are encouraged in verse form. When learning through playtime is complete, calming down for rest is encouraged through use of the rhymes in the "Now It's Time To Rest" section.

> These twos, and threes, and fours
> Can do a lot of things.
> They hop, skip, and walk.
> They dance, sing, and talk.
> Through movement, song, and rhyme,
> Each day's a learning time.

ALL ABOUT ME

ME

I can do
A lot of things.
With my ears I hear,
With my mouth I sing.
With my nose I smell,
With my eyes I see.
With my hands and feet
I can climb a tree.

MY BODY

(Can be sung to the tune of "This Old Man")

Here's my head.
It is round.
I can move it
Up and down.
It's on my body,
So come and see:
It's the perfect
Size for me.

Here are my eyes,
One and two.
They are looking
Now at you.
They're on my face,
So come and see:
They're the perfect
Ones for me.

Here's my hair
On my head.
Some have brown, and
Some have red.
It's on my head,
So come and see:
It's the perfect
Color for me.

Here's my nose.
With it I tell
When there is
A funny smell.
It's on my face,
So come and see:
It's the perfect
Size for me.

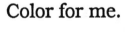

I have ears,
One and two.
They can listen
When I talk to you.
They're on my head,
So come and see:
They're the perfect
Size for me.

I have hands,
One and two.
I can clap
And wave them, too.
They're part of my body,
So come and see:
They're the perfect
Ones for me.

Here's my mouth.
It is round.
It can laugh,
Or it can frown.
It's on my face,
So come and see:
It's the perfect
One for me.

Here are my shoulders,
One and two.
Moving them
Is fun to do.
They're on my body,
So come and see:
They're the perfect
Ones for me.

I have feet,
One and two.
Come and see
What they can do.
They're part of my body,
So come and see:
They're the perfect
Size for me.

SIT QUIETLY DOWN

(Can be sung to the tune of "Ten Little Indians")

Touch your head and
Touch your nose.
Touch your eyes and
Touch your toes.
Touch your elbow,
Spin around.
Make your body
Sit right down.

I shake my head
And my body, too.
I can do it,
So can you.
I spin my body
All around.
Then I sit
Very quietly down.

Shake one arm and
Then shake two.
Shake my hand:
How do you do?
Shake your body,
Spin around.
Make your body
Sit quietly down.

HURRY, DON'T BE SLOW

(Can be sung to the tune of "Row, Row, Row Your Boat")

Have the children touch the various parts of their bodies as they sing. Each time try to sing and move a little faster.

Head,
Shoulders,
Knees
And toes —
Moving, now let's go!
Spin around
And clap your hands —
Hurry, don't be slow.

Eyes,
Ears,
Mouth
And nose —
Touch them, now let's go!
Spin around
And clap your hands —
Hurry, don't be slow.

PARTS OF MY BODY

(Can be sung to the tune of "Up On The Housetop")

This is my body,
It's all mine —
My head,
My shoulders,
My waist,
My spine.

My legs,
My hands,
My feet,
My knees.
Put them all together
And you have me.

Eyes and nose
On my face,
Everything
In the right place.
I shake my body and
    turn around —
Then my body
    sits quietly down.

TOUCH AND TELL

Come and touch
Your head with me.
Touch your nose
And touch your
   knee.

Touch your ears,
Your neck,
Your hair.
Spin around now
In the air.

Come and touch
Your elbows, now.
Hands on hips
And take a bow.

Touch your leg,
Your arms, and toe,
And soon
Your body parts
You'll know.

BODY PARTS

(Can be sung to the tune of "Frère Jacques")

Arms and elbows,
Arms and elbows,
Wrists and hands,
Wrists and hands.
Shake your little fingers,
Shake your little fingers,
If you can,
If you can.

Legs and knees,
Legs and knees,
Ankles and feet,
Ankles and feet.
Move your little toes,
Move your little toes,
Keep the beat,
Keep the beat.

14

SPINNING, SPINNING, ALL AROUND

(Can be sung to the tune of "If You're Happy and You Know It")

Take your hands and
Shake them in the air,
Take your hands and
Shake them in the air.
You can shake them all around,
Clap and have them make a sound,
Take your hands and
Shake them in the air.

Take your arms and
Spin them like a plane,
Take your arms and
Spin them like a plane.
You can move them up and down,
You can move them 'round and 'round.
Take your arms and
Spin them like a plane.

Take your head and
Move it up and down,
Take your head and
Move it up and down.
You can make it go around,
Shake it now without a sound,
Take your head and
Move it up and down.

Take your body and
Spin it like a top,
Take your body and
Spin it like a top.
Spinning up or spinning down,
Rolling 'round upon the ground,
Take your body and
Spin it like a top.

15

MY HEAD

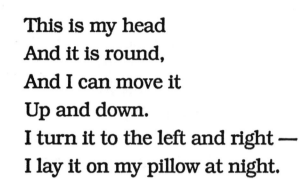

This is my head
And it is round,
And I can move it
Up and down.
I turn it to the left and right —
I lay it on my pillow at night.

MY NECK

This is my neck,
And it is long.
It holds my head,
So it must be strong.

If I had a neck
Like a big giraffe,
Everyone would stare
And they would laugh.
My neck is small,
The right size, you see,
'Cause I'm not a giraffe —
I'm only me.

HAIR

I have hair
Upon my head.
Mine is brown,
But Mom's is red.

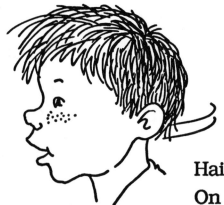

Hair can be short,
Hair can be long,
Brown, or black, or
Red or blonde.

Hair's like spaghetti
On a clown.
It shakes all over
When he falls down.

A HAIRCUT

She said it wouldn't hurt,
But I didn't want to go.
If I got my hair cut
I knew it wouldn't grow.

Now that I am here,
It's really lots of fun,
Sitting in the big chair,
Watching everyone.

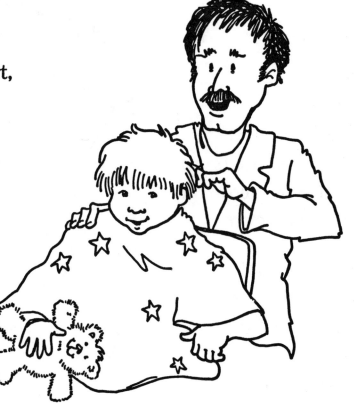

EYES

I have two eyes
And they are blue.
I can count them,
One and two.

With my eyes,
I can see
All the things
Surrounding me.

I have two eyes
And they are brown,
And I can move them
Up and down.

EARS

Ears, ears,
I have two.
Come and see
What they can do.
They hold my earmuffs
When it's cold,
And listen to things
That I am told.

Ears help you hear
A lot of things,
The television,
And birds that
    sing.

I have two ears
Just right for me,
On the sides of my
    head
Where they ought
    to be.

MY FEET

(Can be sung to the tune of "Three Blind Mice")

My little feet,
My little feet.
See what they do,
See what they do.
They are jumping up
    and down,
They are dancing all
    around,
They are skipping on
    the ground —
My little feet,
My little feet.

TWO FEET

I have two feet,
One and two —
They know exactly
What to do.
They carry me around,
Having lots of fun.
With them I skip,
I walk, I run.

MY ELBOW

I hurt my elbow
When I was home,
And mommy called it
My funnybone.
I know she's wrong,
And I'll tell you why —
It didn't make me laugh,
It made me cry!

HANDS

(Can be sung to the tune of "Six Little Ducks")

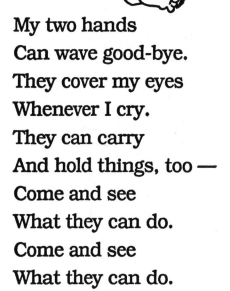

I have two hands,
One and Two.
Come and see
What they can do:
Clap, and catch
And throw a ball,
And they can help me
If I fall.
And they can catch me
If I fall.

My two hands
Can wave good-bye.
They cover my eyes
Whenever I cry.
They can carry
And hold things, too —
Come and see
What they can do.
Come and see
What they can do.

MY LITTLE HANDS

My little hands
Can clap clap clap.
My little fingers
Can snap snap snap.
My little hands
Can reach for the sky.
My little hands
Can wave good-bye.

My little hands
Can bounce a ball.
My little hands
Can help me crawl.
My little hands
Can climb a tree.
My little hands
Stay right by me.

EATING

Food is good for you,
It helps you grow.
Eat it all,
And don't be slow.
Put it in your mouth
And close your mouth tight.
Chew it ten times
And swallow it right.
Take a drink
And before you know,
Your food is all gone
And off you go!

Vegetables are good for you!
Take one bite, then
Maybe two.
Crunch, crunch, crunch
And chew, chew, chew —
Swallow fast,
It's fun to do.

When I eat food
That I don't like,
I pretend I'm a lion
And take a bite,
For I must grow big,
For I must be strong —
And pretty soon
My food is all gone.

BRUSH YOUR TEETH

(Can be sung to the tune of "Row, Row, Row Your Boat")

Brush-brush-brush
Your teeth,
Do it now with me.
Inside, outside,
Up and down,
They're clean as they can be.

Brush-brush-brush
Your teeth,
Chase the plaque away.
Up and down
And all around —
Make them white today.

PLAYING TOGETHER

(Can be sung to the tune of "Here We Go 'Round The Mulberry Bush")

This is the way we
   share our toys,
Share our toys,
Share our toys.
This is the way we
   share our toys,
When we play
   together.

This is the way we
   build our house,
Build our house,
Build our house.
This is the way we
   build our house,
It's fun to do it
   together.

Suggestions for other verses:
This is the way we race our cars.
This is the way we help at home.
This is the way we clean our room.
This is the way we roll the ball.

SHARING

When my friend comes
To my house to play,
I'll share my toys
With her (him) today.

I'll take a turn
And so will she (he) —
We'll play together
Happily!

PUTTING TOYS AWAY

(Can be sung to the tune of "Row, Row, Row Your Boat")

After playing with my toys,
I clean up everything.
I always have a lot of fun
'Cause here's the song I sing:

Now it's time to tidy up
And put my toys away —
I pick them all up from
    the floor,
I'm finished for today.

CLEANING UP

(Can be sung to the tune of "London Bridge")

All my toys
I put away,
Put away,
Put away.
All my toys
I put away —
Save them for another day.

PHONE

Ring, ring,
It's the phone.
I answer it
When I'm at home.
I'm very polite,
I say "hello,"
Then I get my mom
And off I go.

NEW WORDS

There are some new words
That I know
Because I'm bigger
And I'm starting to grow.

I say "thank you"
And I say "please"
And I say "excuse me"
When I sneeze.

PLEASE

(Can be sung to the tune of "I'm A Little Teapot")

PLEASE is a new word
That I've learned today.
PLEASE is a new word that
   I like to say.
PLEASE may I go out, and
PLEASE pass the bread.
I never just say "give me,"
I say PLEASE instead.

THANK YOU

(Can be sung to the tune of "I'm A Little Teapot")

THANK YOU's something new
I've learned to say.
THANK YOU's something new
I learned today.

When I get a gift
I say THANK YOU,
I say it just because
It's the proper thing to do.

LEARNING MY ABC'S

A B C D
E F G
H I J K
L M N O P
Q R S T
U and V
W X Y and Z

Pages 31 through 56 may be used for directed teaching, and also as pages for a take-home Alphabet Book. Help the children color page 29 to be used as a booklet cover. Each day enjoy one action rhyme and sing its letter song to the tune of "Row, Row, Row Your Boat." Save the pages as each letter is

explored. The completed ABC booklet will reinforce letter recognition as well as serve as a treasured early-learning memento.

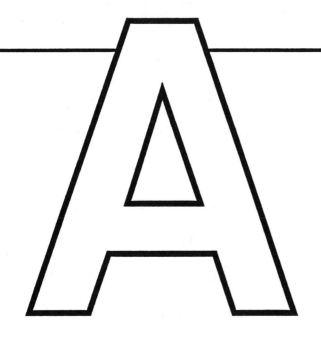

This is the letter A.
Say it now with me
    today —
A is for apple,
A is for ape,
A funny-looking ape
In a polka-dot cape.

SING OUT A

Alligator, Ant, and Ape —
All these start with A.
The alphabet is fun to do,
Let's do A today.

Adam, Anna, Anthony
Are names with A, you see.
If your name begins with A,
Stand up now with me.

31

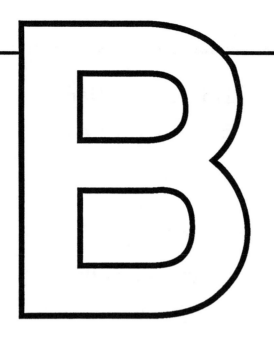

B

This is the letter B.
Come and say it now
with me —
B is for bubbles,
B is for bear,
A funny-looking bear
All covered with hair.

SING OUT B

Bird, Beaver, Bat and Ball —
All these start with B.
The alphabet is fun to do,
Come do it now with me.

Brendon, Billy, Betsy, Bob
Are names with B, you see.
If your name begins with B,
Stand up now with me.

32

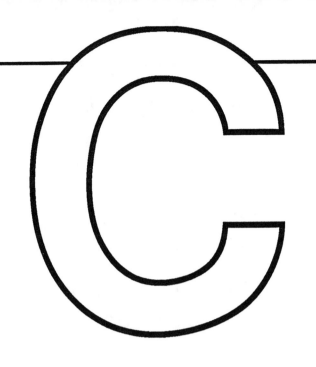

C

This is the letter C.
Come and say it now
    with me —
C is for candy,
C is for cat,
A funny-looking cat
Who is wearing a hat.

SING OUT C

Cake, Cookies, Coat, and Cap —
All these start with C.
The alphabet is fun to do,
Come do it now with me.

Cindy, Catherine, Charlie, Cam
Are names with C, you see.
If your name begins with C,
Stand up now with me.

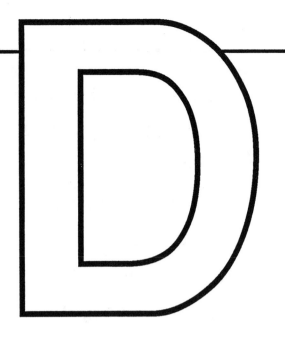

This is the letter D.
Come and say it now
    with me —
D is for dinosaur,
D is for dog,
A funny-looking dog
Who likes to jog.

SING OUT D

Doll, Dish, Deer, and Duck —
All these start with D.
The alphabet is fun to do,
Come do it now with me.

Darryl, David, Debbie, Dan
Are names with D, you see.
If your name begins with D,
Stand up now with me.

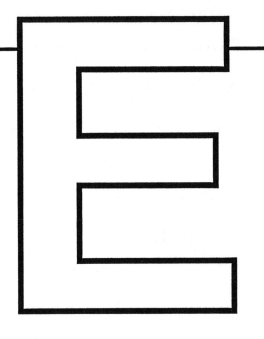

This is the letter E.
Come and say it now
    with me —
E is for elephant,
E is for elf,
A funny-looking elf
Sitting on a shelf.

SING OUT E

Eat, Eggs, Elbow, Eight —
All these start with E.
The alphabet is fun to do,
Come do it now with me.

Emma, Eve, Eden, Ed
Are names with E, you see.
If your name begins with E,
Stand up now with me.

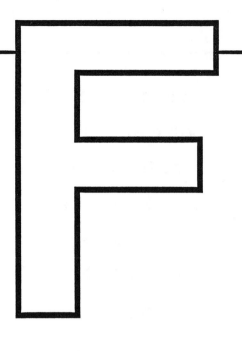

F

The letter F is fun, you see.

Come and say it now
 with me —
F is for fishing,
F is for frog,
A funny-looking frog
Sitting on a log.

SING OUT F

Fun, Food, Fingers, Face —
All start with F, you see.
The alphabet is fun to do,
Come do it now with me.

Ferris, Francis, Fletcher, Frank
Are names with F, you see.
If your name begins with F,
Stand up now with me.

36

This is the letter G.
Come and say it now
   with me —
G is for girl,
G is for giraffe,
A funny giraffe
Who can make you laugh.

SING OUT G

Gumdrops, Grandma, Gate, and Goat —
All these start with G.
The alphabet is fun to do,
Come do it now with me.

Gina, Garrett, Gabrielle
Are names with G, you see.
If your name begins with G,
Stand up now with me.

37

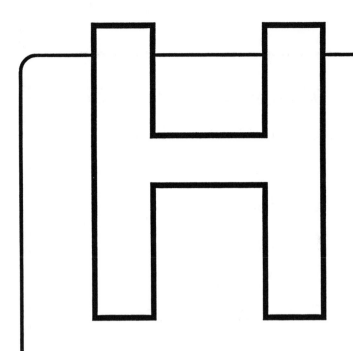

H

The letter H is fun, you see.
Come and say it now
  with me —
H is for hippo,
H is for house,
A tiny little house
Just right for a mouse.

SING OUT H

Hat, Hug, Horse, and Hill —
All start with H, you see.
The alphabet is fun to do,
Come do it now with me.

Hannah, Harley, Heidi, Hank
Are names with H, you see.
If your name begins with H,
Stand up now with me.

38

The letter I is fun, you see.

Come and say it now

 with me —

I is for igloo,

I is for ice.

In wintertime,

Skating on ice is nice.

SING OUT I

Ice Cream, Icicle, Indian, Ink —

All start with I, you see.

The alphabet is fun to do,

Come do it now with me.

Ian, Ivan, Isabelle

Are names with I, you see.

If your name begins with I,

Stand up now with me.

—— 39 ——

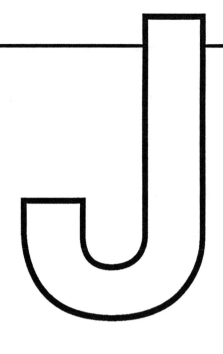

This is the letter J.
Say it now with me
        today —
J is for jumping,
J is for John.
John is my friend,
And we play on my lawn.

SING OUT J

Jelly, Juice, Jacket, Jog —
All these start with J.
The alphabet is fun to do,
Let's do J today.

Jana, Jen, James, and John
Are names with J, you see.
If your name begins with J,
Stand up now with me.

40

K

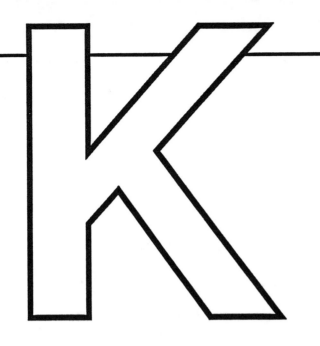

This is the letter K.
Say it now with me
today —
K is for kangaroo,
K is for kite.
I never fly
My kite at night.

SING OUT K

Ketchup, Kick, Key, and King —
All these start with K.
The alphabet is fun to do,
Let's do K today.

Kathie, Kirk, Kristen, Ken
Are names with K, you see.
If your name begins with K,
Stand up now with me.

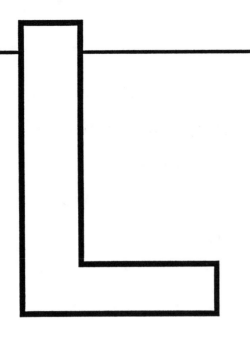

The letter L is fun, you see.
Come and say it now
 with me —
L is for leprechaun,
L is for lamb,
A woolly little lamb
Whose name is Pam.

SING OUT L

Lion, Little, Look, and Love —
All start with L, you see.
The alphabet is fun to do,
Come do it now with me.

Lana, Larry, Lia, Luke
Are names with L, you see.
If your name begins with L,
Stand up now with me.

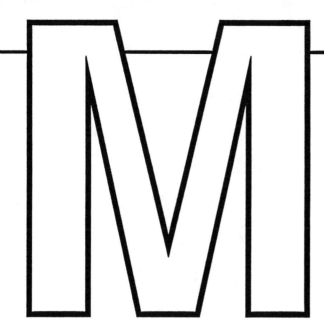

The letter M is fun, you see.
Come and say it now
    with me —
M is for monkey,
M is for mouse,
A funny little mouse
Running 'round our house.

SING OUT M

Mommy, Mop, Mice, and Man —
All start with M, you see.
The alphabet is fun to do,
Come do it now with me.

Maggie, Matthew, Mark, and May
Are names with M, you see.
If your name begins with M,
Stand up now with me.

43

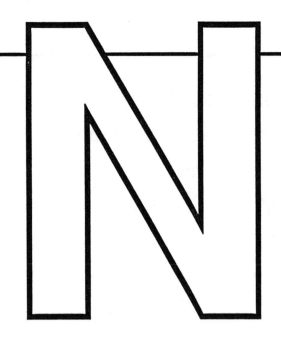

N

The letter N is fun, you see.
Come and say it now
   with me —
N is for napping,
N is for night.
I always turn off
My light at night.

SING OUT N

Name, Nest, Nine, and No —
All start with N, you see.
The alphabet is fun to do,
Come do it now with me.

Nicholas, Nada, Newton, Ned
Are names with N, you see.
If your name begins with N,
Stand up now with me.

44

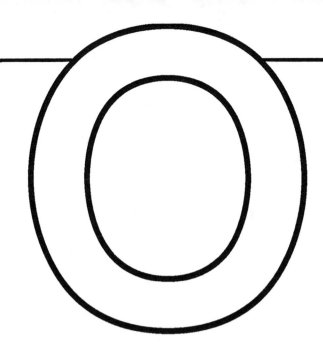

O

The letter O is fun, you see.
Come and say it now
    with me —
O is for octopus,
O is for ox,
A great big ox
Standing on a box.

SING OUT O

Open, Old, On, and Out —
All start with O, you see.
The alphabet is fun to do,
Come do it now with me.

Oscar, Owen, Olivia
Are names with O, you see.
If your name begins with O,
Stand up now with me.

— 45 —

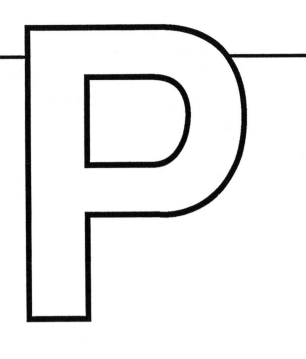

P

This is the letter P.
Come and say it now
   with me —
P is for peanuts,
P is for pig,
A funny little pig
That can dance a jig.

SING OUT P

Popcorn, Party, Pet, and Punch —
All these start with P.
The alphabet is fun to do,
Come do it now with me.

Patrick, Peter, Patti, Paul
Are names with P, you see.
If your name begins with P,
Stand up now with me.

46

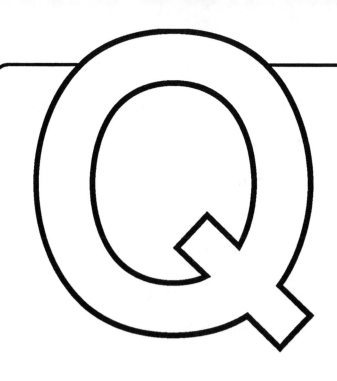

The letter Q is fun, you see.
Come and say it now
   with me —
Q is for quiet,
Q is for quack.
A duck can quack
With feathers on his back.

SING OUT Q

Quick, Queen, Quarter, Quit —
All start with Q, you see.
The alphabet is fun to do,
Come do it now with me.

Quentin, Queenie, Quinlan, Quince
Are names with Q, you see.
If your name begins with Q,
Stand up now with me.

SHHHH

47

R

The letter R is fun, you see.
Come and say it now
   with me —
R is for rabbit,
R is for rat,
A funny-looking rat
With a big striped hat.

SING OUT R

Ring, Red, Rug, and Run —
All start with R, you see.
The alphabet is fun to do,
Come do it now with me.

Rob, Rebecca, Randy, Rick
Are names with R, you see.
If your name begins with R,
Stand up now with me.

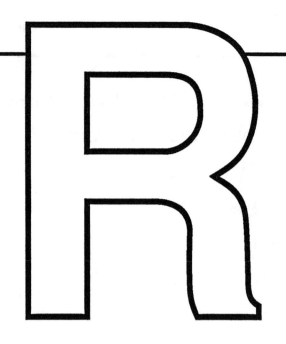

S

The letter S is fun, you see.
Come and say it now
    with me —
S is for snowman,
S is for sun.
In the warm sun
I can play and run.

SING OUT S

Snake, Sunshine, Song, and Sand —
All start with S, you see.
The alphabet is fun to do,
Come do it now with me.

Sandy, Sally, Sean, and Scot
Are names with S, you see.
If your name begins with S,
Stand up now with me.

49

T

This is the letter T.
Come and say it now
with me —
T is for turtles,
T is for toad,
A funny-looking toad
Hopping down the road.

SING OUT T

Tree, Top, Tickle, Ten —
All these start with T.
The alphabet is fun to do,
Come do it now with me.

Tammy, Tara, Tina, Todd
Are names with T, you see.
If your name begins with T,
Stand up now with me.

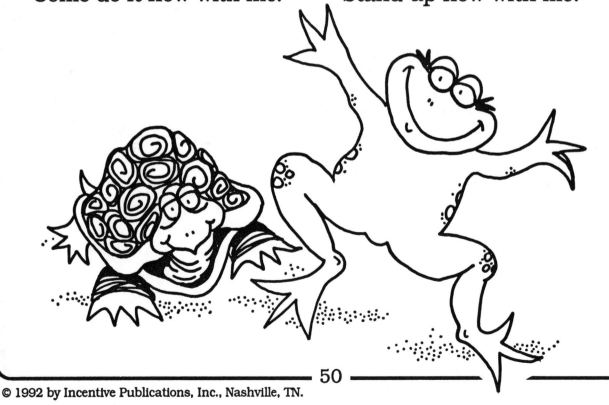

50

The letter U is fun, you see.

Come and say it now

with me —

U is for umbrella,

U is for us.

When there is just us,

We go on the bus.

SING OUT U

Uncle, Up, and Unicorn —

All start with U, you see.

The alphabet is fun to do,

Come do it now with me.

Unis, Una, Ursula

Are names with U, you see.

If your name begins with U,

Stand up now with me.

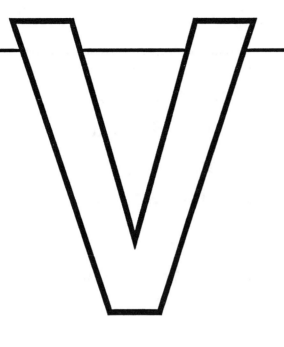

This is the letter V.
Come and say it now
with me —
V is for vegetables,
V is for vest,
My polka-dot vest that
I like the best.

SING OUT V

Van, Visit, Vacuum, Vote —
All these start with V.
The alphabet is fun to do,
Come do it now with me.

Vickie, Vance, and Valerie
Are names with V, you see.
If your name begins with V,
Stand up now with me.

52

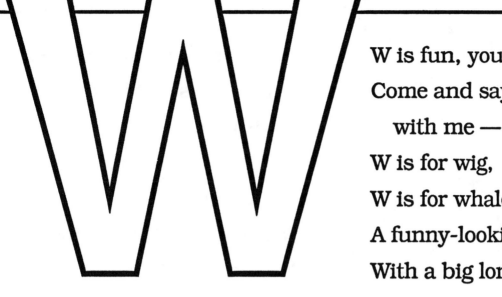

W is fun, you see.
Come and say it now
with me —
W is for wig,
W is for whale,
A funny-looking whale
With a big long tail.

SING OUT W

Wet, Water, Wash, and Wear
Start with W, you see.
The alphabet is fun to do,
Come do it now with me.

Warren, Wayne, Wendy, Will
Are names with W, you see.
If your name begins with W,
Stand up now with me.

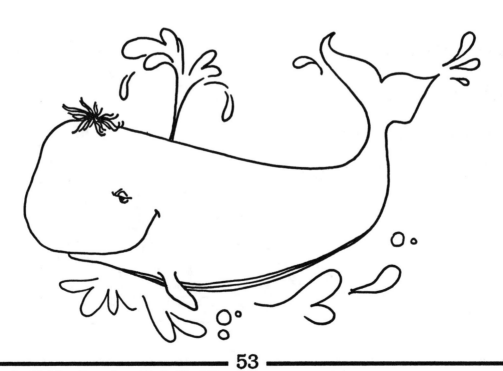

53

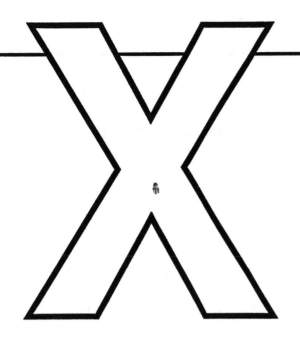

The letter X is fun, you see.

Come and say it now

with me —

X is for xylophone,

X is really fine.

You make an X by drawing

Two straight lines.

SING OUT X

Xylophone and X-ray —

Both start with X, you see.

The alphabet is fun to do,

Come do it now with me.

Xavier and Xenia

Are names with X, you see.

If your name begins with X,

Stand up now with me.

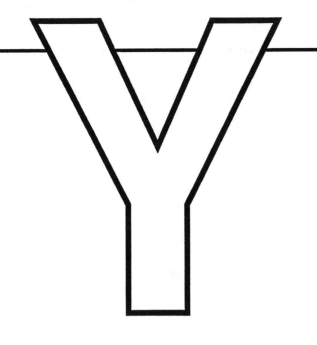

The letter Y is fun, you see.
Come and say it now
    with me —
Y is for yellow,
Y is for yak,
A funny-looking yak
With hair on his back.

SING OUT Y

Yard, You, Yell, and Yes —
All start with Y, you see.
The alphabet is fun to do,
Come do it now with me.

Yvette, Yvonne, Yolanda, Yul
Are names with Y, you see.
If your name begins with Y,
Stand up now with me.

— 55 —

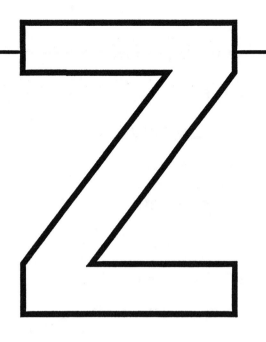

Z

This is the letter Z.
Come and say it now
with me —
Z is for zebra,
Z is for zoo.
Going to the zoo
Is fun to do.

SING OUT Z

Zero, Zap, Zipper, Zoom —
All these start with Z.
The alphabet is fun to do,
Come do it now with me.

Zoe, Zelda, Zachariah
Are names with Z, you see.
If your name begins with Z,
Stand up now with me.

THE ALPHABET SONG

(Can be sung to the tune of "Mary Had A Little Lamb"; sing l-m-n-o-p quickly)

A B C D E F G

E F G

E F G

A B C D E F G

Say them now with me.

H I J K L M N O P

L M N O P

L M N O P

H I J K L M N O P

Say them now with me.

Q R S T U and V

U and V

U and V

Q R S T U and V

Say them now with me.

W X and Y and Z

Y and Z

Y and Z

W X and Y and Z

It's easy as can be.

KNOWING MY NUMBERS

COUNT TO TEN

(Can be sung to the tune of "If You're Happy And You Know It")

Come and play with me
    right now
And count to ten.
Come and play with me
    right now
And count to ten.
Clap your hands
And you will see,
It's as easy as can be.
Come and play with me
    right now
And count to ten.

1, 2, 3, 4, and 5.
1, 2, 3, 4, and 5.
6–7–8–9–10,
When we're done
We'll start again.
Come and play with me
    right now
And count to ten.

FREEMONT THE FROG

Freemont Frog
Is here today
To show you how to work,
To show you how to play!
Now that he's older
He's starting to grow,
And there are some things that
   he wants to know:
Colors and shapes,
Letters A to Z,
And counting numbers, 1 - 2 - 3.

So come along with me
And we'll have some fun,
And together we'll see
Just how it's done.

Freemont's numbers
Are lots of fun —
Count his friends
That have a one.
Only one frog
Do I see.
I'll take him now
To play with me.
One little frog
All alone —
Don't be sad,
I'll take you home.

ONE

(Can be sung to the tune of "I'm A Little Teapot")

I have just one nose and
One mouth, you see —
One belly button, just
    for me.
I have one body
And one little head,
And I go to sleep in
One little bed.

ACTION RHYME

One, one,
Here we go.
Hurry up
And don't be slow.
Make your body
Into a One.
Roll on the floor
And have some fun.
Shake one arm
And one leg too,
Hop on one
Like a kangaroo.
One, one,
Now we're through.
Come with me
And we'll count
To Two.

ONE

When I'm all alone
And there's only one,
I get sad and
I don't have fun.
But sometimes ONE
Is really best
'Cause when mommy
    bakes,
I get the rest.

2

Freemont Frog
Will count with you.
Help him find the number two.
One, two do I see
Freemont's Friends play happily.

Two little frogs
Having lots of fun —
Come and count them
One by one.

TWO

(Can be sung to the tune of "I'm A Little Teapot")

I have just two ears and
Two eyes to see.
Here are two hands
And two feet for me.
Two arms and two legs,
And now I'm done.
Come on over and
We'll have some fun.

ACTION RHYME

Two, Two,
Here we go.
Hurry up,
Don't be slow.
Clap your hands
And count to two.
Tap your feet
Inside your shoe.
Swing your
Two arms
Way up high.
Turn around
And try to fly.
Two, Two,
Come and see
If we now
Can count to
Three.

TWO

There are lots of things
That come in two's,
Like purple socks and
Brand-new shoes.
Things also come
In pairs, you see,
like twins and pants
And glasses for me.
But I like two
When I'm at home —
Then I will not be
All alone.

3

Freemont's here	1 - 2 - 3 frogs	Count the frogs
And now we'll see	In the sun,	That have a three —
If we can find	Hopping 'round and	Come and count to three
The number THREE.	Having fun.	With me.

THREE

(Can be sung to the tune of "I'm A Little Teapot")

I have just three buttons
On my coat.
I have three sailboats
That can float.
There are three
In my family —
Mommy and Daddy
And then there's me!

THREE

My two friends come to play with me
And altogether there are three.
Three sugar cookies and three drinks, too.
Three is the number after two.
Sometimes they spend the night with me,
And mommy comes to tuck in three.

ACTION RHYME

Three, Three,
Here we go.
Hurry up
And don't be slow.
Clap your hands
Three times with me.
Stamp your feet
And count to three.
Shake your body
Just for fun
Now three times
'Round the room
You run.
Do three
    somersaults
In a row
Pretty soon
Number 3 you'll
    know.
Three, three,
Add one more.
Now we'll do
The number four.

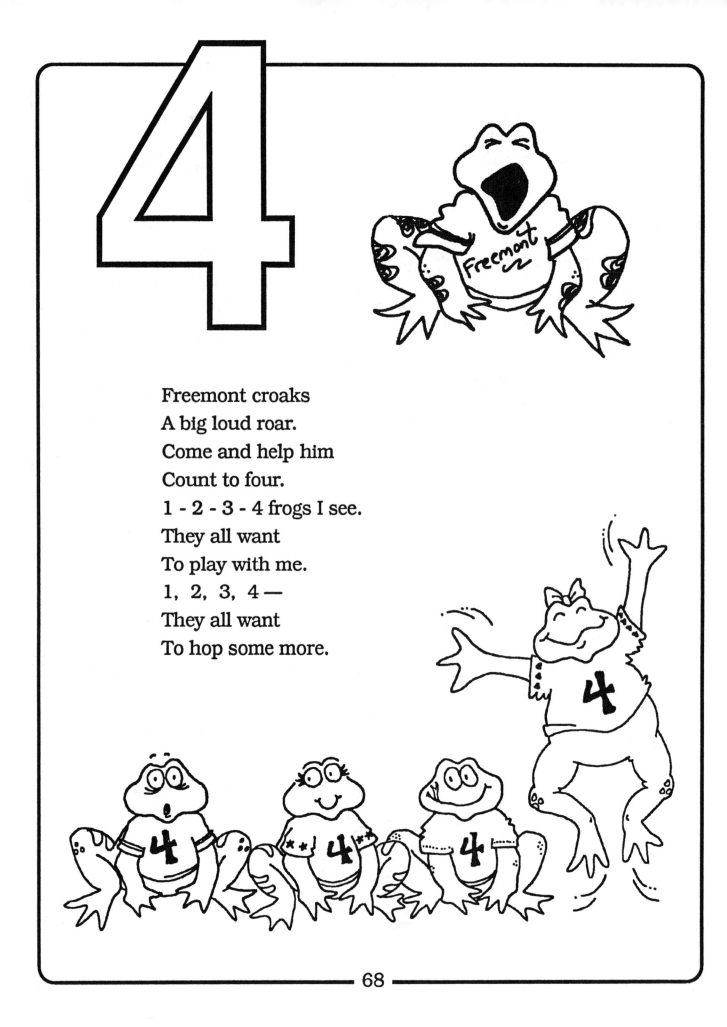

Freemont croaks
A big loud roar.
Come and help him
Count to four.
1 - 2 - 3 - 4 frogs I see.
They all want
To play with me.
1, 2, 3, 4 —
They all want
To hop some more.

FOUR

(Can be sung to the tune of "I'm A Little Teapot")

In my little family
There are four —
Mommy and daddy,
And two more.
Four is the age
That I want to be.
Come and count to four
  with me.

FOUR

1, 2, 3, 4
Little puppies on
  the floor.
1, 2, 3, 4
Puppies running
  out the door.
1, 2, 3, 4
I want to play with
  them some more.

ACTION RHYME

Four, Four,
Here we go.
Hurry up and
Don't be slow.
Clap your hands
And count to four.
Stamp your feet
Hard on the floor.
1, 2, 3, 4 —
Spin around the
Floor some more.
Jump four times
All in a row,
And pretty soon
Number 4 you'll
  know
4, 4, you're alive.
Now we'll do
  the number 5.

5

Freemont's here.
He just arrived.
Come and count
The frogs to five.

Five little frogs
Do we see,
Coming now to
Count with me.

5, 4,
3 - 2 - 1 —
Little frogs are
Having fun.

FIVE

(Can be sung to the tune of "Row, Row, Row Your Boat")

1, 2, 3, 4, 5 —
Birds up in a tree.
Watch them flying all around,
Landing next to me.

ACTION RHYME

Five, Five,
Here we go.
Hurry up
And don't be slow.
Count five fingers,
Count five toes.
Shake them all and
Here we go.
Clap five times
Snap five times, too.
Five is lots of
Fun to do.
Five, five,
We are through.
6 is next
For us to do.

FIVE

Five little fingers
In a row.
They can walk, now
Watch them go.
Five little fingers
Curl up tight —
Wave good-bye
And say goodnight!

Freemont's friends
Can hop on sticks.
Count the ones
That have a 6.

Six, Six do I see.
Come and
Count them
Now with me.

1, 2, 3 —
4, 5, 6!
Six little frogs
Hopping on some sticks.

FINGERPLAY

1 little frog,
Sad and blue.
Another came along,
And then there were 2.

2 little frogs,
Happy as can be.
Another came along,
And then there were 3.

3 little frogs,
Croaking some more.
Another came along,
And then there were 4.

4 little frogs,
Trying to dive.
Another come along,
And then there were 5.

5 little frogs,
Picking up sticks.
Another came along,
and then there were 6.

6 little frogs,
Hopping all around,
In the water
and on the ground.

SIX

1, 2, 3,
4, 5, and 6 —
Counting frogs and
Counting sticks.
6, 5, 4, 3, 2,
And 1 —
Counting can be lots
of fun.

ACTION RHYME

Six, Six,
Here we go.
Hurry up, now
Don't be slow.
Count to six
And march around.
Slowly six times
Touch the ground.
Wiggle five fingers
And one big toe.
Six is the number
You want to know.
Seven is next and
we will see
If you can count to
seven with me.

7

Freemont's friends	Seven little frogs	1, 2, 3, 4,
Are here, you see.	Are having fun.	5, 6, 7.
Count to seven	You can count them	Little frogs
Now with me.	One by one —	Can count to 7.

SEVEN

(Can be sung to the tune of "London Bridge")

1, 2, 3, 4, 5, 6, 7 —
5, 6, 7 —
5, 6, 7 —
1, 2, 3, 4, 5, 6, 7 —
Turn around and
Point to heaven.

ACTION RHYME

Seven, Seven,
Here we go.
Hurry up and
Don't be slow.
Count to seven
And stamp
Your feet.
Clap your hands
And keep the beat.
Shake your hands
And your body, too.
Seven is lots
Of fun to do.
Jump up high
And count to seven.
Stretch your arms
Up high to heaven.
Seven is done,
I can hardly wait
For us to do
The number eight.

SEVEN

Seven silly snowmen
Standing in the sun —
Before they melt,
Let's have some fun.

Seven slippery snakes
All around —
Slipped away
And couldn't be found.

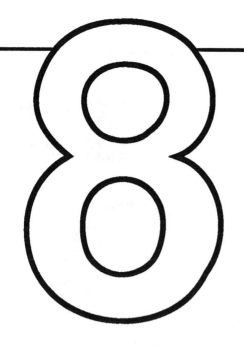

Freemont frog
Can hardly wait
To help you
Count to number 8.
Eight little frogs
Hopping up and down,
In the water and all around.

1, 2, 3, 4,
5, 6, 7, 8 —
Little frogs, now
Don't be late.
Come and count
To 8 with me.
It's as easy as can be.

EIGHT

(Can be sung to the tune of "Row, Row, Row Your Boat")

1, 2, 3, and 4
5, 6, 7, 8 —
Come and count
With me right now.
Hurry, don't be late.

ACTION RHYME

Eight, Eight,
Here we go.
Hurry up and
Don't be slow.
Be a spider
On the floor.
Move your hands
And feet some more.
Be a spider
On the wall.
Use your arms
And legs to crawl.
Count to eight
And you'll be fine —
Then we'll do
The number nine.

EIGHT

Eight little spiders
In a row —
Watch them dance,
Watch them go.
Eight long legs
Has each little one,
Moving all around
And having fun.

1 - 2 - 3 - 4
5 - 6 - 7 - 8!
Counting can be
Really great.

Freemont's friends are really fine.
Count the ones that have a 9 —
Nine little frogs, in the sun,
Sitting on lily pads,
Having fun.
1, 2, 3, 4, 5,
6, 7, 8, and 9.
Come and help me
Count to nine,
If you have
The time.

NINE

(Can be sung to the tune of "Here We Go 'Round The Mulberry Bush")

Come and help me
   count to nine,
Count to nine,
Count to nine.
Come and help me
   count to nine,
And soon you'll know
Nine fine!

1, 2, 3, 4, 5,
6, 7, 8, and 9 —
Turn around and
Say this rhyme,
And soon you'll know
Number nine just fine.

ACTION RHYME

Touch your head,
Touch your toes,
Touch your ears,
Touch your nose,
Touch your mouth,
Touch your spine,
Sit right down
And count to nine.

ACTION RHYME

Nine, Nine,
Here we go.
Hurry up, now
Don't be slow.
1, 2, 3, and 4 —
Be like frogs,
Hop out the door.
5, 6, 7 - 8 - 9 —
Little frogs
Can count just fine.
Clap nine times,
Stamp your feet.
Counting can be
Really neat.
Turn and count to nine again —
Then we'll do the number ten.

10

Freemont's here
To count again.

Count his friends
That have a ten —
Ten little frogs
Do I see.
Come on over
To count with me

1, 2, 3 - 4 - 5,
6, 7, 8 - 9 - 10!
Counting
Little frogs again.

COUNT TO TEN AGAIN

(Can be sung to the tune of "Row, Row, Row Your Boat")

1, 2, 3, 4 - 5 —
6 - 7 - 8 - 9 - 10!
Clap your hands and
Stamp your feet —
Count to ten
Again!

FINGERPLAY

1 little frog
Sitting in the sun,
2 little frogs
Having lots of fun,
3 little frogs
Hopping all around,
4 little frogs
Sitting on the ground.
5 little frogs
Moving in a line,
6 little frogs
Looking just fine,
7 little frogs
Having fun at play,
8 little frogs
Hopping away,
9 little frogs
Skipping free,
10 little frogs
To play with me.

AGAIN, OH!

(Can be sung to the tune of "B.I.N.G.O.")

Freemont frog
Had some friends,
And they could count
To ten, oh!

1, 2, 3 - 4 - 5 —
6, 7, 8 - 9 - 10 —
Clap your hands
And turn around,
And count to ten
Again, oh!

With number ONE,
There is lots you
    can do —
Cut and paste and
Color it blue.

Stick on stars and
Trace on the lines,
And soon you'll know
Number ONE just
    fine.

Trace the number
    TWO with me,
It's as easy as can be.
You can color, cut,
    and paste
This TWO next to
The ONE you traced.

I'll count the
    numbers
Now with you,
And soon you'll
    know
The number
    TWO.

Come and look
And you will see —
We are doing
Number THREE.
Trace the THREE
Along the lines,

Color it
If you have time.
Now you're through,
So come with me,
And we will count
From one to THREE.

Here's a great big
Number FOUR.
Help me trace
The lines once more.
Take some colors and
go over the lines —

Now your FOUR
Will look just fine.
Cut and color,
And you'll see,
FOUR is easy as
    can be.

Here is the number
    FIVE to do —
You can trace and
    cut and glue.
FIVE is tricky,
So take your time.

Follow the dots
And you'll do fine.
Now, trace over
The great big FIVE,
And number FIVE
Will come alive.

Make the SIX
With just one line.
Follow the dots
And you'll be fine.
Inside the SIX
There is a space

Where you can make
A happy face.
Trace the SIX
And then you'll see,
You can count
To SIX with me.

SEVEN is easy
For you to do —
Trace the lines
And color them, too.
Big number SEVEN
Is easy, you see.

Color it in
Right now with me.
Follow the lines
Across and down
And in the space
You can color it brown.

Trace the EIGHT
Around the lines.
Count to EIGHT
And take your time.
Color the EIGHT
With red and blue —

EIGHT is not
So hard to do.
Two circles together
Look like an EIGHT.
Do it now, for
It can't wait.

If you trace
Along the lines,
You will make
The number NINE.
With this number
You can color, too,

Cut and paste,
Or make it blue.
Have some fun and
Take your time.
When you do
The number NINE.

Come and help me
Make this TEN.
Trace the lines
With me again.
Make a line,
A circle, too —

TEN is not so
Hard to do.
TEN, TEN,
Now we're through,
And I'll come
And count with you.

NOW IT'S TIME
TO REST

QUIET TIME

It's quiet time
So I must go —
I'll hurry up,
I won't be slow.
I'll jump and
   shake
And spin around,
And then I'll sit
Without a sound.

REST TIME

Use this action rhyme to introduce the "Rest Time" songs on the next seven pages. All the verses may be sung to the tune of "I'm A Little Teapot." Have the children act like the animals (or train, or airplane) as they sing and settle down to rest.

When it's Naptime
Or it's Quiet Time,
I can be anything,
Singing this rhyme.

I can be a bear
Stomping all around,
But once I am resting
I don't make a sound.

NAP TIME

I'll be a bunny
And I'll hop to bed,
And on my pillow
I'll lay my head.
I'll close my eyes
And shut them tight
And stay in bed
And sleep all night.

QUIET TIME

I'll be a bunny
And I'll hop around.
When it's time to stop,
I won't make a sound.
I'll sit down
Very quietly.
This is the place
Where you'll find me.

NAP TIME

Now I'll be a snake
And I'll slide into bed,
Wiggle under the covers,
And lay down my head.
Very soon the wiggles
Will be out of me,
And I'll fall asleep
Very peacefully.

QUIET TIME

I'll be a snake
And I'll crawl on the floor,
Slither around,
And slide some more.
But when it's time to stop,
I won't make a sound.
In my quiet place
I will be found.

A TURTLE

NAP TIME

I'll be a turtle,
I'll move very slow,
And into bed
Is where I'll go.
The blankets on the top
Will be my house,
And I'll be as quiet
As a mouse.

QUIET TIME

I'll be a turtle,
Watch me go
Around the floor —
I'll move very slow.
But when it's quiet time,
I'll crawl in my house,
And I'll be as quiet
As a mouse.

NAP TIME

I'll be a duck,
I'll waddle into bed.
I won't talk,
I'll quack instead.
Under the blankets
I'll tuck my beak,
I'll close my eyes,
And go to sleep.

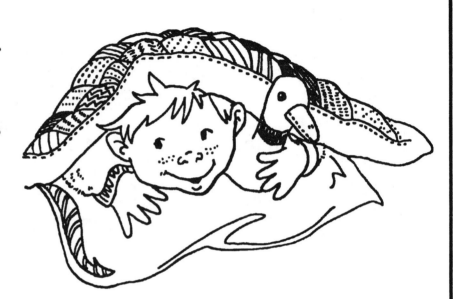

QUIET TIME

I'll be a duck,
I can move and quack.
I have feathers
On my back.
When it's quiet time,
I won't waddle away.
In my resting place
Is where I'll stay.

NAP TIME

I'll be an elephant,
Moving slow,
Swinging my long trunk
High and low.
I'll roar like an elephant
And say goodnight,
Pull up the covers,
And turn off the light.

QUIET TIME

I'll be an elephant
Moving around,
Swinging my large trunk
Up and down.
When it's time to stop
I'll sit right down,
And in my quiet place
I'll be found.

NAP TIME

I'm a little train
And I'm off to bed.
I don't talk,
I chug instead.
I turn my wheels
And I move real slow —
Chug-a-chug-a-choo-choo,
Off I go!

QUIET TIME

I'm a little train
On the track, you know.
Chug-a-chug-a-choo-choo,
Off I go!
When it's quiet time,
I'll move real slow,
I'll sit right down,
And I will not go.

AN AIRPLANE

NAP TIME

I'm a little airplane,
I'm off to bed.
I don't walk,
I fly instead.
My wings can soar
And I fly around
Into my bed
Without a sound.

QUIET TIME

I'm a little airplane,
I'll fly around,
Moving my big wings
Up and down.
When it's time to rest,
I'll land on the ground —
This little airplane
Won't make a sound.

A BEDTIME SONG

(Can be sung to the tune of "Up On The Housetop")

It is time to go to bed —
Hop right in!
Pull the cover up
To your chin.
Lay your head down,
Snuggle up tight,
Close your eyes,
And say goodnight.

Oh, oh, oh!
Don't you know?
While you sleep
Your body grows.
When you wake,
It's a brand-new day
With lots of time
To run and play.

NAP TIME

Naptime can be
Lots of fun —
Come and see
How it is done.
Hop on one foot
Up and down,
Touch your nose,
Touch the ground.
Shake your body,
Shake your head,
Then shake yourself
Into your bed.
Now lie very still,
Don't make a sound.
Close your eyes,
Don't move around.
Pull the cover up real tight
And very quietly say good-night.